Little Charles Hits a Home Run!

Simple steps to prevent and detect skin cancer

By Mary Mills Barrow and
Charles E. Crutchfield III, MD

Illustrations by Laurie Sigmund
Introduction by Maryellen Maguire-Eisen

BEAVER'S POND
PRESS

eaver's Pond Press, Inc.
08 Ohms Lane
dina, MN 55439-2129
952) 829-8818
ww.BeaversPondPress.com

ISBN: 978-1-59298-472-5

Library of Congress Control Number: 2012908257
Book design by Mayfly Design
Printed in the United States of America
Third Printing: 2016

20 19 18 17 16   6 5 4 3

Foreword

As a parent, I have overheard children on ball fields requesting a break from midday sun, only to be told by their coach to "get back out there and don't worry about getting sunburned." As an oncology and dermatology nurse, I know that more than half of all children experience sunburns annually and that there is a link between childhood sunburns and melanoma. I know that we cannot afford to be nonchalant about exposing children to this significant health risk. Ignorance and complacency on the part of parents, coaches, and caretakers in general play a major role in this problem.

There will be more than 3 million new cases of skin cancer in the United States this year. These numbers are expected to continue to rise. The fact is, there are more skin cancers diagnosed each year than all other cancers combined. Melanoma, the most deadly form of skin cancer, is increasing in all segments of our society, including Latinos, African Americans, and children.

Melanoma accounts for 1–3 percent of all pediatric cancers,[1] while 90 percent of pediatric melanoma cancers occur in girls ages ten to nineteen.[2] These staggering statistics punctuate the importance of sun protection education being introduced to children at a young age.

SunAWARE Hits a Home Run makes an important contribution to this effort by highlighting three important messages about the prevention and early detection of skin cancer for parents and children:

1. Skin cancer is related to overexposure to natural and artificial sources of ultraviolet radiation.
2. Skin cancer is preventable.
3. Skin cancer is curable if diagnosed and treated early.

The SunAWARE acronym provides five easy action steps for parents, teachers, coaches, health-care providers, and community leaders to follow when educating children about prevention and early detection. SunAWARE has been endorsed by many leading health-care organizations. I believe that it is the responsibility of caretakers to provide children with current information and action steps to protect them against sun damage and the risk of skin cancer. By being SunAWARE, children can play outdoors safely and parents can have peace of mind knowing that their children are protected from a major health risk.

Be Safe. Be SunAWARE!

—Maryellen Maguire-Eisen
Executive Director
Children's Melanoma Prevention Foundation

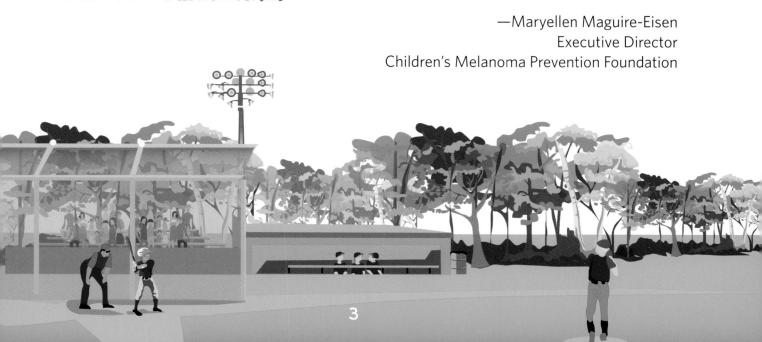

"Okay, team," Coach shouted, waving his clipboard to get the attention of the twelve Little League players waiting restlessly in the dugout for the start of the next inning. "You're doing great. Now drink some water. Check your gear, and let's go over positions."

Charles and Isaac picked up their mitts and found a place on the bench. They were best friends. They lived next door to each other, went to the same school, played on the same teams, and always sat together.

"Don't forget to put your cap back on," Isaac whispered.

Charles nodded as he grabbed his cap from under the bench where he'd thrown it when going out to bat. He then unzipped his sports bag and pulled out a new sunscreen stick. "Here. My dad said to remind you to rub this on your face and arms," he said, handing the stick to Isaac.

"I already put sunscreen lotion on before the game," Isaac replied. "No way am I getting sunburned like I did last week."

"You'd better rub on some more," another boy, Connor, whispered. "My mom says even one burn is bad for you, and you have to reapply sunscreen at least every two hours to be safe."

"Yeah," agreed Charles.

"Charles," the coach interrupted. "You play right field. Connor, take second base, and Isaac, you pitch. Now listen, everyone, we're only one run ahead. If we can keep them from scoring now, at the top of the sixth inning, then we will easily keep our lead when we're up to bat. We're doing great out there, so keep it going."

Charles walked slowly out to right field, all the while smacking his fist into his glove. *Right field is too quiet*, he thought as he looked over at the bleachers and saw his mom and dad sitting next to Isaac's parents. He smiled and waved, still wishing Coach had given him a base position.

It was late morning, and the sun felt hot. Charles pushed back his cap and wiped his brow with his wristband. *Sun rays are most powerful between the hours of 10 a.m. and 4 p.m.*, he thought, remembering a conversation at the cookout with Isaac's family the night before. *If you can't AVOID being in the sun between 10 a.m. and 4 p.m., you have to use protection.*

Charles's dad is a *dermatologist* (a doctor who takes care of skin), and Isaac's dad is a *meteorologist* (a person who studies the atmosphere and the weather).

During the cookout, they had explained all about the sun and the many ways sun rays keep us warm and healthy, but can harm us if we are not careful. They both agreed that everyone should know the five easy steps in **SunAWARE** to stay safe and healthy while playing in the sun.

SunAWARE

Avoid unprotected exposure to sunlight, seek shade, and never indoor tan.

Wear sun-protective clothing, including a long-sleeved shirt, pants, a wide-brimmed hat, and sunglasses, year-round.

Apply broad-spectrum sunscreen with a sunburn-protection factor (SPF) of 30 or greater to all exposed skin, and reapply every two hours or as needed.

Routinely examine your whole body for changes in your skin and report concerns to parents or health-care providers.

Educate your family and community about the need to be SunAWARE.

Be Safe. Be SunAWARE, Charles thought as he turned towards the pitcher's mound and took his position in right field. *It is pretty easy to remember **A-W-A-R-E.***

"Strike one," the umpire called.

Charles kicked the dust and repositioned his feet. Isaac was pitching.

"You can do it!" Charles called out.

"Yeah!" Connor cheered from second base.

"Strike two."

Charles bounced on his toes. "Come on," he whispered. "Pitch it fast."

A moment later, the sound of the bat smacking the ball echoed around the field. The ball flew low and hard. It bounced behind Isaac on the pitcher's mound and past the outfielder who had run forward to catch it. The batter ran to second and stood next to Connor.

"Darn," Charles muttered as he settled back into his position. "Isaac will be mad about that."

Charles felt the warmth of the sun on his arms and noticed that Connor's arms were turning pink. It reminded him of the cookout and the first letter in AWARE.

A: Avoid unprotected exposure to sunlight, seek shade, and never indoor tan.

"Why do sun rays burn our skin?" Isaac had asked as they sat around the picnic table. "And why is that bad? Doesn't a sunburn or tan just go away?"

"Those are good questions," Isaac's dad answered. "First, remember that the sun is a star, and like all stars it produces *ultraviolet radiation*, or UVR."

"What's that?"

"UVR is the waves or rays of energy that come from the combination of hot gases that make up the sun. Some of these rays are so long they reach through space and hit the planets around the sun. Two kinds of those rays, UVA and UVB, hit the earth, and when we are outside those rays can be absorbed by our skin."

"So when a person is outside too long and absorbs too much UVA or UVB," added Charles's dad, "their skin can get burned or tanned, which can cause *premature aging* or health problems such as *skin cancer*."

"Can anything stop the rays from hitting the earth?"

"A layer of gas called *ozone* between six and thirty miles above the earth stops a lot of it. But not enough for us to be safe."

Did you know?

There are three types of ultraviolet radiation: UVA, UVB, and UVC. Humans must protect themselves from UVA and UVB. UVC does not reach the earth's surface.

UVB

UVA

UVC

OZONE LAYER

Did you know?

The sun, like all stars, is a huge ball of gases, mostly hydrogen with about 10 percent helium and other elements.

10

"But how do we know if the UVR is getting through the ozone?"

Again, Isaac's dad answered. "Well, we can see some of the ultraviolet radiation because it is in the form of light. And we can use the *UV index* to tell us how much UVR will get through the ozone on any day. In fact, the UV index was created so that we would know how much protection we need every day. "

The UV Index and Corrrespoding Sun Precautions

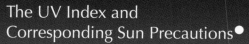

Global UV Index	Rating	Recommended Precautions
1 - 2	Low	
3 - 5	Moderate	
6 - 7	High	
8 - 10	Very High	
11+	Extreme	

- UV range less than 2 is low, and no protection is required.
- UV range 3–5 is moderate, which requires protection. Seek shade during midday hours.
- UV range 6-7 is high, which requires protection. Seek shade during midday hours.
- UV range 8–10 is very high, which requires extra protection. Avoid being outside during midday hours.
- UV range 11 is extreme and requires caution. Avoid being outside during midday hours.

Did you know?

The seasons change depending on the way the earth tilts. During summer, the Northern Hemisphere is tilted towards the sun; the days are longer as the sun appears higher in the sky. More sun rays reach the ground, increasing the need for protection.

Did you know?

You can find the UV index for your city and state at the websites of the National Weather Service (http://www.weather.gov) and the Environmental Protection Agency (www.epa.gov). You can also find it on your local newspaper's website.

"But not everyone gets sunburned easily," Isaac stated. "Why do guys like me and Connor get red when we're outside too long, and Charles gets darker brown?"

"Charles has more melanin in his skin than you, Isaac. Melanin is what gives skin its color. When sun rays shine on the skin, special skin cells called melanocytes start producing more melanin. The melanin absorbs and blocks ultraviolet radiation, kind of like an umbrella. The more melanin the body produces, the darker the skin appears. This is what happens when a person gets tan. But don't be fooled! Some people think a tan looks good, but it's really your body's way of telling you that your skin is being damaged and needs protection. Tans are bad!"

"And you are right, Isaac, not everyone gets easily burned," Charles's dad continued. "Your friend Connor, for example, gets more tan than pink. But the sun can damage anyone's skin. If you have fair skin, you may burn more quickly and damage your skin more easily because you don't have as much melanin in your skin for protection. But even the darkest skin is not safe from ultraviolet damage. No matter what color your skin is, you should always use sun protection and check your skin. Skin cancer occurs with all *skin types*. Remember, everyone should be SunAWARE!"

Skin Types

I. Always burns easily, never tans, and is extremely susceptible to damage caused by sun exposure including all skin cancers, particularly melanoma.

II. Almost always burns, rarely tans, and is highly susceptible to damage caused by sun exposure including all skin cancers, particularly melanoma.

III. Sometimes burns moderately, tans moderately and uniformly, and is susceptible to damage caused by the sun, including melanoma and all other skin cancers.

IV. Less likely to burn and tans easily, but skin may be damaged by sun exposure and is still at risk for all skin cancers, including melanoma.

V. Tans easily and rarely burns, but skin may be damaged by sun exposure and is still at risk for all skin cancers, including melanoma (particularly on parts of body not easily exposed to the sun: palms of hands, soles of feet, and mucous membranes).

VI. Does not burn, although skin may be damaged by sun exposure, and is still at risk for all skin cancers, including melanoma (particularly on parts of body not easily exposed to the sun: palms of hands, soles of feet, and mucous membranes)[3].

When they had been at the cookout, Isaac's mom, who is a *pediatrician* (a doctor who treats children), handed each of the boys a hamburger. "You know," she said, "there are lots of risky things that can cause skin cancer. Being exposed to too much sun is the biggest risk of all, but there are other risks. I have a list I give to parents, and I'll give you a copy to take home so you can read it and keep it in a notebook (see "Resources" section for more information)."

Charles looked around the field as he waited for the next batter. He remembered that Isaac's mother had seemed puzzled when she said, "What really bothers me is that one of the biggest risk factors for skin cancer is fashion. Can you believe it? A lot of teenagers and some older people think being tan looks cool, so I tell them how UVR can hurt their skin, and some of them still go out and use tanning beds. The skin we are born with is already beautiful, so I don't understand why anyone would want to change their color."

"Oh boy," Charles had whispered to Isaac. "My dad gets really mad about tanning beds."

"'Tans are a symptom of damaged skin," Charles's dad immediately responded. "The light bulbs or tanning bulbs used in tanning beds emit UVA, which burns differently than UVB and penetrates the skin more deeply. This type of damage causes skin cancer. California has banned the use of tanning beds by anyone under the age of eighteen. Many other states are working to pass similar laws—just like the laws for cigarettes. I wish all people, but especially teenagers, would stop using tanning beds and simply enjoy the color of the skin they were born with."

Did you know?

- Most people who use tanning beds are young women aged seventeen to twenty-nine[4].
- Using a tanning bed even once can increase your chance of getting melanoma by 75 percent.[5]
- The number of cases of melanoma among young women rose 50 percent between 1980 and 2004.[6]

Did you know?

California was the first state to ban the use of tanning beds by people under the age of eighteen.

"I like staying in the shade best," said Charles's mom, who was sitting under the table's umbrella with his little sister, Arianna, on her lap. "Shade is so easy! Trees provide shade, and so do umbrellas and dugouts. In fact, I wish there were more *shade sails* at schools and at the baseball parks. Shade helps keep us cool, and when you wear sun-protective clothing and sunscreen while in the shade, you get all the sun protection you need."

Did you know?
Trees with thick, wide-spreading, dense leaf canopies provide great natural shade.

Did you know?
Sun rays bounce from the ground, water, and other surfaces like the side of the house, so you should always use sun protection even while in the shade.

She is right, Charles thought, looking back over the field. *It's much cooler in the shade than out on the field, where there is no shade.*

"Heads up, Charles!" Coach yelled.

And at just that moment, a fly ball hit by a lefty landed about three feet away from Charles. Charles ran, picked it up, and threw it to Connor on second base before the hitter could leave first.

"That's the way, Charles!" he heard his father yell with pride.

"Go, Charles!" his older sister, Olivia, yelled from the sidelines, where she and Arianna sat with Connor's sister, Jessie. All three girls were wearing hats, sunglasses, and long-sleeved shirts, which reminded Charles of the next letter in SunAWARE.

W: Wear sun-protective clothing, including a long-sleeved shirt, pants, a wide-brimmed hat, and sunglasses, year-round.

Did you know?
Sun-protective clothing is recommended as the first step for effective sun protection by organizations around the world dedicated to preventing skin cancer.

Yep, my sisters are protected! Charles thought with a smile. He rubbed his fist in his baseball mitt and watched Isaac warm up his arm.

On the next pitch, the batter smacked the ball, and it arched toward the outfield so high that Charles had to shield his eyes to see it. "I wish I had my sunglasses," he muttered. His dad had said sunglasses were important for protecting eyelids as well as the eyes themselves. Charles just wanted to block the glare so he could see the ball, but he was glad to know sunglasses would protect his eyes from UVA and UVB rays.

The American Academy of Pediatrics recommends the use of sunglasses for babies who are older than six months, toddlers, and young children.[7]

Always check labels to make sure sunglasses block at least 97 percent of UVR, both UVA and UVB. Be sure your sunglasses fit correctly.

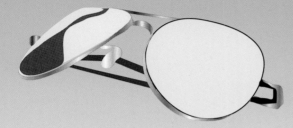

Did you know?

Brown eyes are damaged by the sun as easily as blue or hazel eyes, which means everyone should wear sun glasses.

As the ball flew toward him, Charles remembered seeing photographs of children wearing hats with flaps over the backs of their necks. *They look cool*, he thought as he held out his glove to make the catch.

"You're out!" the umpire called.

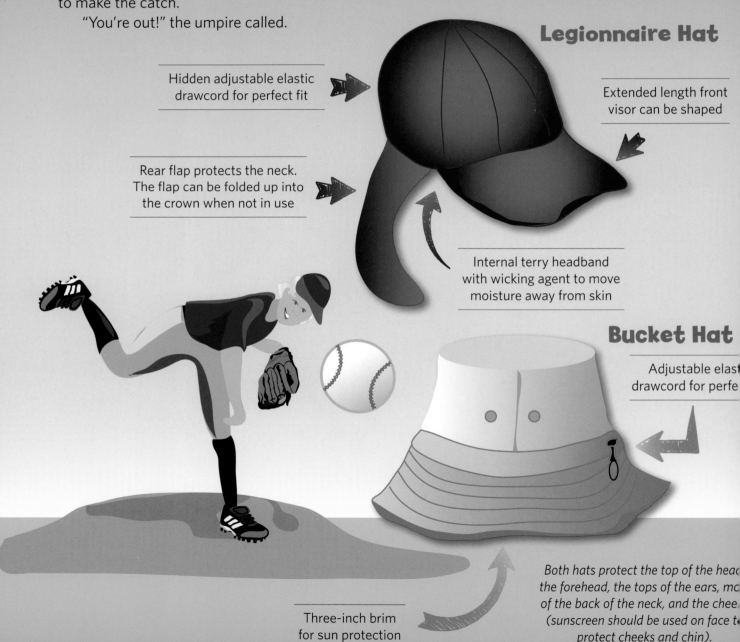

Legionnaire Hat

Hidden adjustable elastic drawcord for perfect fit

Extended length front visor can be shaped

Rear flap protects the neck. The flap can be folded up into the crown when not in use

Internal terry headband with wicking agent to move moisture away from skin

Bucket Hat

Adjustable elast drawcord for perfe

Three-inch brim for sun protection

Both hats protect the top of the head the forehead, the tops of the ears, mo of the back of the neck, and the chee (sunscreen should be used on face t protect cheeks and chin).

Hats for All Ages

There are many types of hats, but not all are sun protective. The hats shown below offer excellent sun protection. Look for labels that guarantee a UV-protection factor (UPF) of 50+.

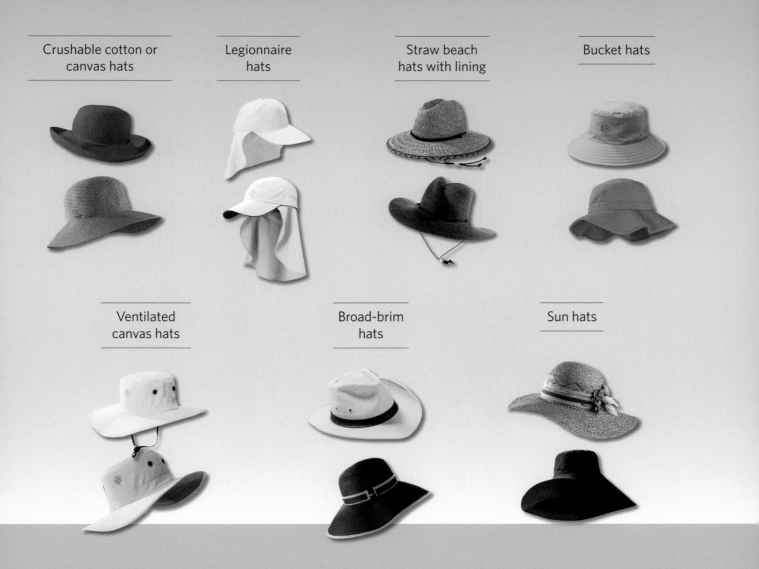

Crushable cotton or canvas hats

Legionnaire hats

Straw beach hats with lining

Bucket hats

Ventilated canvas hats

Broad-brim hats

Sun hats

Charles tossed the ball to Isaac, who gave him a thumbs-up before turning to the next batter.

A girl with long braids beneath her helmet dragged her bat to the mound and got ready for the pitch. Charles smiled. He knew Emily. She was in his class at school, and he really liked her.

Charles had first noticed Emily at recess one day when she was rubbing a sunscreen stick over her face. He'd asked her if she liked sunscreen sticks more than lotion.

"I like them about the same," she answered before she ran off to join her friends.

He thought about the next letter in SunAWARE:

A: Apply *broad-spectrum* sunscreen with a sunburn protection factor (SPF) of 30 or greater to all exposed skin, and reapply every two hours or as needed.

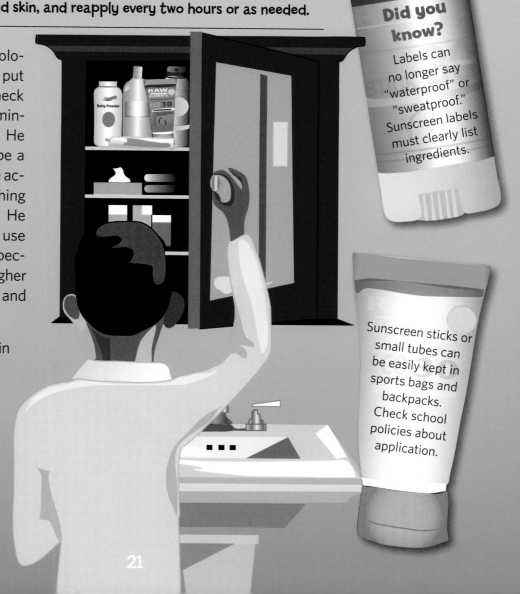

Charles's dad, the dermatologist, tells his patients to put sunscreen on their face, neck and other exposed skin 15 minutes before going outside. He says sun protection should be a daily habit for people who are active and outdoors—like washing hands or keeping teeth clean. He also says that people should use sunscreen labeled broad spectrum, with an SPF of 30 or higher to protect against both UVA and UVB rays.

"Keep sunscreen with you in your sports bag or backpack so you can reapply every two hours," he advises. "Remember to reapply sunscreen after swimming. And only use sunscreen on a baby under six months on rare occasions when you are unable to find shade and have no other protection.

Did you know? Labels can no longer say "waterproof" or "sweatproof." Sunscreen labels must clearly list ingredients.

Sunscreen sticks or small tubes can be easily kept in sports bags and backpacks. Check school policies about application.

I hope she doesn't hit it over here, Charles thought as Emily made a practice swing.

Isaac pitched, and Emily hit a fly ball long and hard into the outfield. The crowd went crazy as she ran from one base to the next. When she passed Charles, he couldn't help but notice that her arms were a reddish color. *Doesn't she know she needs to protect her whole body?* Charles worried. *I need to tell her.*

As Emily ran for home base, Charles looked over at his dad, trying to come up with a way to tell Emily why sun protection is important. Then he realized that he should tell her whole team about it—both teams, in fact!

I know, he thought, *if I get Dad to show us how to look at our freckles and moles, he could also explain that sun protection helps to keep the sun from hurting out skin. He could show us how to…*

R: Routinely examine your whole body for changes in your skin and report concerns to parents or health-care providers.

The Children's Melanoma Prevention Foundation recommends that young children learn to identify their moles and freckles. Teens (and adults) should learn to perform routine body checks and report concerns to parents or health care professionals.

Items needed for body check:

- Body-check chart
- Well-lighted room
- Two chairs
- Two mirrors, one full-length and one handheld
- Blow dryer
- Comb
- Notebook
- Pencil

In the notebook, keep track of the number of moles on your skin, their sizes, and their locations. Take photographs to make it easier to describe any changes to your physician.

Keep copies of the ABCDEs of Melanoma and the measurement guide at the front of the notebook, and compare your moles to the illustrations each month. Put a date on the notes, and get your parents to help you put down the exact number and size of the moles. Encourage your parents to check their skin too!

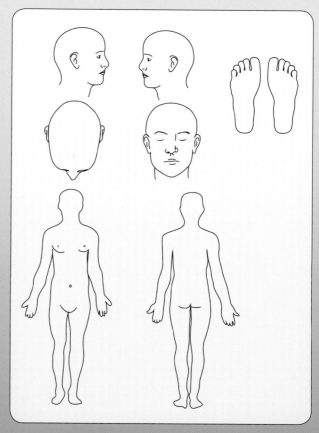

Body-check chart. Courtesy of American Academy of Dermatology.

If you have a sore that does not heal in three weeks, report it to your doctor.

How to Perform a Body Check

1. Start with the face (especially the nose), arms, and hands (including fingernails and between the fingers). Raise your arms and use the mirror to examine the backs of your upper arms (including underarms). Take notes.
2. Work from the top down. Using the blow dryer and a comb, make parts through your hair—one row at a time—over the top of your head and down to your ears to check for any lesions covered by hair. You can check the back of your head using a handheld mirror, but this is difficult. Ask someone to help. Take notes.
3. With your back to a full-length mirror, use the handheld mirror to check your neck (front and back) shoulders, chest, and torso. Check the upper back and sides. Women should check the undersides of the breasts. You may want to use a checklist so you don't forget any areas. Take notes.
4. Still using both mirrors, check your lower back, the backs of both legs, and buttocks. Take notes.
5. Sit down, prop each leg in, turn on a second chair, and check the front and sides (thigh to shin), ankles, the tops of feet, between the toes, and under the toenails. Examine the heels and soles of feet. Use a checklist to be sure you have covered everything. Take notes.
6. Still sitting, again prop each leg in, turn on a second chair, and use a handheld mirror to examine the genitals. Take notes.

Once you complete the entire body check, enter all the information in your notebook with a date. This is especially important for those at high risk of melanoma, those who are monitoring changes for a doctor, and those who are helping to monitor others. Check your risk factors on the list found under "Resources" at the back of this book.

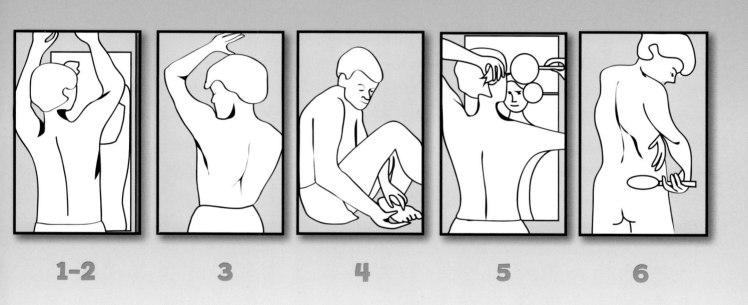

1-2   3   4   5   6

What to Look For: The ABCDEs of Melanoma

The ABCDEs of Melanoma was developed by the American Academy of Dermatology so everyone can easily understand what to look for when conducting self-examinations.

A: Asymmetry. Draw an imaginary line down the middle of any mole and ask yourself if the two halves match. Ordinary moles are usually round and symmetrical, while melanomas are often asymmetrical—the two halves are different.

B: Border. Ordinary moles are round or oval-shaped and have well-defined, smooth, even borders. Melanomas often have irregular, uneven, or notched borders.

C: Color. If your mole has several colors—such as black, brown, red, white, or blue—or an irregular pattern of colors, it may be melanoma.

D: Diameter. Watch for changes in the size of your moles.

E: Evolving. A mole that changes in size, shape, shades of color, surface, or symptoms may be melanoma. Furthermore, if a mole tingles, itches, burns, or feels strange, it may be evolving and should be checked.

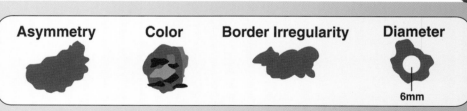

| Asymmetry | Color | Border Irregularity | Diameter |

6mm

Ordinary moles are generally less than six millimeters (a quarter of an inch) in diameter, or about the diameter of a pencil eraser. Melanomas may be as small as an eighth of an inch, but they are often much larger.

Keep a copy of this page in your notebook.

The next two batters struck out. As the teams changed places, Charles ran over to his parents. "Emily has a sunburn. And a bunch of the other kids look like they are getting burned, too."

"Here," his mom said, taking two large tubes of sunscreen from her tote bag. "Tell them to rub this on."

Charles ran first to his coach to get permission. He then gave one tube of lotion to Connor, who promised to make sure everyone on their team put it on their arms, chins, and cheeks, the tops of their ears, and the backs of their necks. Then he ran to the other team and gave the other tube to Emily.

"Thanks, Charles. I hate sunburn." She rubbed the lotion on her arm. "You've really saved the day," she whispered, smiling.

Charles pulled his cap down over his eyes and turned away shyly. *Well, not quite,* he thought as he ran back to his own team.

"I gotta get Coach to tell everybody's parents to put sunscreen on before going out in the sun, and all about what SunAWARE means. That's what the **E** says to do."

E: Educate your family and community about the need to be SunAWARE.

Coaches can encourage use of sun-protective uniforms and sunscreen.

Health and science classes can include SunAWARE curriculum.

Parents can help develop sun-protection policies within schools and for sporting programs.

The media can use SunAWARE for sun-protection advice.

Schools, daycare centers, and camps can introduce hat programs.

Families can use SunAWARE advice at home.

Sun-protection legislation can be introduced for all children.

Rejoining his team, Charles stood silently next to Isaac while Coach listed the batting order. Everyone was excited and nervous. They were now two runs behind, but they knew they had a good chance of winning. Isaac would bat first, followed by Connor, and then Charles.

"Hit it hard!" Charles encouraged Isaac, who followed his advice and hit a single on the first pitch.

"Yes!" Charles shouted, jumping up and down as Isaac ran to first and Connor moved to the batter's box. "Go, team!"

Next, Connor hit a double, bringing the crowd to its feet. Charles moved up to the plate. He pulled his helmet down tightly on his head, then got his feet into position, and leaned forward with the bat. *I can do this. I can do this.*

"Strike one," the umpire shouted as the ball hit the catcher's mitt.

"You can do it, Charles!" his father called from the stands.

Charles repositioned his feet.

"Come on, Charles!" Isaac and Connor yelled.

The pitch was fast and hard, and the sound of the bat smacking the ball was hollow—perfect! The ball was flying up, up, high, arching over the field toward the fence. Charles ran. He couldn't believe it. He could see Isaac sliding into home base just as he reached first. The ball didn't stop. He could see Connor racing past second and third and his parents standing with their arms in the air. The ball kept going right out of the field. It was a HOME RUN!

The whole team cheered as they crowded around Charles. It had been a perfect SunAWARE game.

Glossary

Broad spectrum: including all the sun rays that reach earth's surface. Broad-spectrum sunscreen offers protection against both UVA and UVB.

Dermatologist: a doctor who specializes in the treatment of skin and its diseases. Dermatologists also take care of problems of the scalp, hair, and nails.

Meteorologist: a scientist who studies the earth's atmosphere. A meteorologist may predict the weather, investigate climate trends, or study the effects of sun rays on the earth's surface.

Ozone: a naturally occurring gas that prevents the sun's harmful rays from reaching the earth by absorbing UVR. The ozone layer forms a thin shield in the stratosphere, a region more than six miles (ten kilometers) above the earth's surface.

Pediatrician: a doctor who specializes in the treatment of children and their illnesses. Pediatricians can also specialize in other medical areas, such dermatology or oncology (cancer treatment), in order to help children with specific illnesses or diseases. A pediatric dermatologist treats the skin and its diseases in children.

Premature aging: a condition in which something grows old faster than it should. Doctors identify overexposure to the sun as the leading cause of age-related skin problems such as wrinkling, dryness, liver spots, and a leathery appearance.

Shade sails: sheets of fabric shaped like a ship's sail and placed on poles or on top of buildings to cast shade over a specific area. Most shade sails are used in gardens, playgrounds, swimming pools, restaurant patios, and other areas where people gather outdoors.

Skin cancer: skin growths with differing causes and degrees of harmfulness. The three most common skin cancers are basal-cell carcinoma, squamous-cell carcinoma, and melanoma. Skin cancer is diagnosed more often than any other cancer.

Skin type: a system for classifying skin based on a person's response to sun exposure. Dermatologists recommend knowing your skin type to help you understand your need for sun protection. People of every skin type need sun protection.

Ultraviolet radiation: sun rays that reach the earth's surface, including UVA and UVB rays. (Another type of sun ray, UVC, is absorbed by the atmosphere and does not reach the earth's surface.)

UV index: a measurement that forecasts the next day's maximum UVR level or peak UV hours. The UV index helps determine what type of sun protection is needed on any given day.

Resources

Body Charts:
American Academy of Dermatology
Melanoma International Foundation: www.melanomaintl.org

UV Index:
Environmental Protection Agency:
www.epa.gov/sunwise/uvindex.html

Shade Devices and Structures:
www.myezshade.com

Skin Cancer Risk Factors:
Mayo Clinic Skin Cancer Risk Factors: www.mayoclinic.com

SunAWARE lessons and curriculum for grades K-12:
The Children's Melanoma Prevention Foundation:
www.melanomaprevention.org

SunAWARE books for children:
www.sunaware.org

Sun-protective clothing with UPF 50+ rating:
www.Coolibar.com

Sunscreens, broad spectrum with ingredients for children's skin:
www.rawelementsusa.com

References

1. Ferrari A, Bono A, Baldi M, et al. Does melanoma behave differently in younger children than in adults? A retrospective study of 33 cases of childhood melanoma from a single institution. *Pediatrics* 2005; 115:649-57. (http://www.skincancer.org/Skin-Cancer-Facts/#pediatrics)

2. Strous JJ, Fears TR, Tucker MA, Wayne AS. Pediatric melanoma: risk factor and survival analysis of the surveillance, epidemiology and end results database. *J Clin Oncol* 2005; 23. (http://www.skincancer.org/Skin-Cancer-Facts/#pediatrics)

3. Pathak, M.K. Jimbo, and T. Fitzpatrick. 1976. Sunlight and melanin pigmentation. In *Photochemical and Photobiologic Reviews*, ed. K. Smith. Vol 1. New York. Plenum.

4. Swerdlow AJ, Weinstock MA. Do tanning lamps cause melanoma? An epidemiologic assessment. *J Amer Acad Dermatol* 1998; 38:89-98.

5. Lazovich D, Vogel RI, Berwick M, Weinstock MA, Anderson KE, Warshaw EM. Indoor tanning and risk of melanoma: a case-control study in a highly-exposed population. *Cancer Epidem Biomar Prev* 2010 June; 19(6):1557-1568.

6. Ibid.

7. American Academy of Pediatrics. Fun in the Sun. 2011 http://www.aap .org/advocacy/archives/tanning.htm

8. Mayo Clinic, Skin Cancer Risk Factors, 11/16/2011 http://www.mayo clinic.com/health/skin-cancer/DS00190/DSECTION=risk-factors

SunAWARE: The Organization and Mission

To combat the epidemic of skin cancer, the United States needs a single, unified, effective, and proactive message to educate the public on preventing and detecting skin cancers. SunAWARE seeks endorsement and collaboration from organizations and businesses to use the SunAWARE acronym as that message. The organization is dedicated to providing skin cancer prevention and detection education for all segments of the population using the five universally accepted steps in the SunAWARE acronym. For more information go to www.sunaware.org.

Skin Cancer Risk Factors

Fair skin: If you have blond or red hair and light-colored eyes, and you freckle or sunburn easily, you are more likely to develop skin cancer.

A history of sunburns: Multiple sunburns as a child or teenager increase your risk of skin cancer as an adult. Sunburns in adulthood are also a risk factor.

Excessive UVR exposure: Anyone who spends too much time in the sun without protection may develop skin cancer. Tanning, including the use of tanning lamps and beds, also puts you at *high* risk.

Sunny or high-altitude climates: People who live in sunny climates or at higher elevations, where the sunlight is strongest, are exposed to more UVR.

Moles: People who have many moles or abnormal moles called dysplasic nevi are at increased risk of skin cancer.

Pre-cancerous skin lesions: Having lesions, or damaged patches of skin, known as actinic keratoses can increase your risk for skin cancer. These are most common on skin that has been sun-damaged.

A family history of skin cancer: If one of your parents or a sibling has had skin cancer, you may have an increased risk for the disease.

A personal history of skin cancer: If you have already had a skin cancer, you're at risk of developing it again.

A weakened immune system: People with weakened immune systems have a greater risk of developing skin cancer. This includes people with certain diseases and people who take immunosuppressant drugs.

Exposure to certain substances: Exposure to certain substances, such as tobacco, alcohol, and arsenic, may increase your risk of skin cancer.

Increasing age: The risk of developing skin cancer increases with age, primarily because many skin cancers develop slowly. The damage that occurs during childhood or adolescence may not become apparent until middle age. But even though skin cancer is more common as we get older, isn't limited to just older people. Skin cancer can occur at any age[8].

About the Authors

Mary Mills Barrow *Founder and Executive Director, SunAWARE*
Mary Mills Barrow is a skin cancer education advocate. She is the creator of the acronym SunAWARE and founder of the SunAWARE organization. The acronym was first introduced in *Sun Protection for Life*, which Barrow coauthored with John Barrow in 2005. The book won the Gold Triangle Award from the American Academy of Dermatology, which recognizes excellence in public education of dermatologic issues. Barrow has since written three Gold Triangle Award-winning books for children using the SunAWARE advice for skin cancer prevention and detection.

Charles E. Crutchfield III, MD
Dr. Crutchfield is a clinical professor of dermatology at the University of Minnesota Medical School. A graduate of the Mayo Clinic Graduate School of Medicine, he holds both a master's degree in molecular biology and genomics and a doctoral degree in medicine. Dr. Crutchfield completed his internship at the Gundersen Clinic and a dermatology residency at the University of Minnesota. He is a board-certified dermatologist and active member of the American Medical Association, National Medical Association, American Academy of Dermatology, and the Alpha Omega Alpha Honor Medical Society. Dr. Crutchfield specializes in pediatric dermatology and in the treatment of skin cancer, acne, psoriasis, and ethnic skin diseases. He is recognized as one of the leading dermatologists in the United States in *Best Doctors in America, 2011–2012* (Best Doctors, Inc.) and was named as one of the Top 10 Dermatologists in the United States by *Black Enterprise* magazine and as one of the Top 21 African American Physicians in the country by the *Atlanta Post*. Dr. Crutchfield is the medical director of Crutchfield Dermatology (www. CrutchfieldDermatology.com). He is an advocate for skin cancer education for people of all colors and in every segment of the population.

Maryellen Maguire-Eisen
Maryellen Maguire-Eisen RN, MSN, is the founder and executive director of the Children's Melanoma Prevention Foundation. She has been a nurse for over thirty years, specializing in both oncology and dermatology. During her career she has cared for people with skin cancer at every stage of the disease. She says, "I have always had difficulty reconciling the loss of someone from skin cancer because it is preventable and easily recognizable. My goal is to prevent skin cancer by teaching children about prevention and early detection." Ms. Maguire-Eisen is an adjunct clinical instructor at Boston University, an American Cancer Society Scholar, and the winner of multiple service and research awards.

Patricia Wilson Crutchfield

Recognizing the need for sun protection education for all people,
and in keeping with the spirit of strong community service and leadership.

The Pat Crutchfield Memorial Fund

www.PatCrutchfieldMemorialFund.com